Class T

By Liza Charlesworth

ISBN: 978-1-339-02778-4

Art Director: Tannaz Fassihi; Designer: Tanya Chernyak
Photos © Getty Images.

1 2 3 4 5 6 7 8 9 10   68   32 31 30 29 28 27 26 25 24 23

Printed in Jiaxing, China. First printing, August 2023.

■SCHOLASTIC

The time is 8:00.
Kids rise and shine.
They line up to ride a bus.

Then, the kids go to class.
At 9:00, they read a tale.
At 10:00, they write.

11:00 is time for math.
It's fun to add on a pad.
Five plus five is ten.

12:00 is time for lunch.
Fish sticks and rice is nice.
It's fun to dine with pals.

5

Kids like 1:00.
They can skip and slide.
They can run and hide.

Sssssss!

Class pets like 2:00.
That is when they get fed.
This snake's name is Mike!

At 3:00, the bell chimes
and kids rush to the bus.
Time to ride back home!